1001 Things to Find

Dinosaurs

igloobooks

Can you find 1001 dinosaur things?

Time explorer twins, Jack and Sophia, have crash landed in Dino Land and their time machine has broken. "I bet the mighty T-rex can help us fix it," says Jack. But, the T-rex has lost her 13 golden eggs and is too sad to help. "Maybe if we find her lost golden eggs, she'll get the other dinosaurs to help fix our time machine?" says Sophia.

Join Jack and Sophia as they hunt for the golden eggs. In each scene, you will need to find Jack, Sophia and a golden egg. There are over 1000 mega items for you to find along the way, too, so let's get exploring!

Jack

Sophia

Golden egg

Let's have a practice first. On the opposite page, see if you can spot Jack, Sophia and the golden egg. Once you've found them, see if you can spot the items below, too.

2 toasty campfires

9 juicy oranges

11 red daisy flowers

Jurassic Jungle

Deep in the jurassic jungle, Jack and Sophia search for the first golden egg. There are so many places to search, that they don't know where to start. Spot Jack, Sophia and a golden egg.

1 thirsty dino

4 spiky spider plants

5 spotty, dotty lizards

6 rainbow mushrooms

7 mouldy apples

8 muddy ant hills

9 angry hornets

10 spiky caterpillars

11 poisonous red vines

13 large bananas

Roaring Waterfall

Splosh! Jack and Sophia dive into the cool water in search of the next golden egg. The dinosaurs are enjoying a splash, too. Can you spot Jack, Sophia and find another golden egg?

- 5 dinos on leaf sunbeds
- 6 jumping fish
- 8 lurking crocodiles
- 12 coconut shell drinks
- 15 exotic lily pads

Treetop Heights

High up in the treetops, the dinosaurs are swinging on the branches, as Jack and Sophia search the canopy for another golden egg. Can you spot Jack, Sophia and a golden egg?

5 swinging dinosaurs

6 white fluffy clouds

8 baby flying pterodactyls

12 large acorns

15 giant snails

Volcano Valley

In Volcano Valley, Jack and Sophia are in a hurry to find the next golden egg before the molten lava catches up with them. Spot Jack and Sophia and then help them to find a golden egg.

1 dinosaur on hot coals

4 hot fountain springs

5 leaf fans

6 bone surf boards

7 cheeky mosquitos

8 fire-breathing lizards

9 meat drumsticks

10 palm trees

11 swirly ammonites

13 human footprints

Dusty Desert

In the dusty desert, Jack and Sophia are busy searching for the next golden egg, but the dinosaurs just want to slide down the sand dunes. Whoosh! Spot Jack, Sophia and a golden egg.

5 bone-shaped clouds

6 dusty tumbleweeds

8 large spiky lizards

12 horned dino skulls

15 flower cactus plants

Pool Playtime

Jack and Sophia are at a rocky pool. Some dinosaurs are hopping across the water and others are trying to catch their dinner. Can you spot Jack, Sophia and a golden egg?

5 dinos catching fish

6 dinosaur rock statues

8 dinos on stepping stones

12 mossy boulders

15 thistle flowers

Stinky Swamp

At the stinky swamp, the dinosaurs are busy bathing in the water and enjoying a leafy lunch, as Jack and Sophia hunt for another egg. Can you spot Jack, Sophia and a golden egg?

1 angry T-Rex

4 rainbow dragonflies

5 pond reeds

6 tree stumps

7 venus fly traps

8 spiky, purple trees

9 juicy pineapples

10 orange bell flowers

11 little, red crabs

13 pink berries

Mountain Mayhem

Jack and Sophia follow the mountain-climbing dinosaurs to the highest peak. It's a long way up but they're sure that they'll find another egg. Spot Jack, Sophia and a golden egg.

5 leaf tents

6 dinos rock-climbing

8 juggling dinos

12 leaf-shaped kites

15 pink birds

Awesome Oasis

It's a sweltering afternoon in the savannah and the dinosaurs are cooling down in the oasis. Jack and Sophia are enjoying a paddle, too. Can you spot Jack, Sophia and a golden egg?

5 super sandcastles

green, spiky dinos drinking

8 flat-top trees

12 large scorpions

15 tropical flowers

Cave Critters

Drip, drip! In a damp, cold cave, there are lots of creepy critters hiding in the shadows. Even some big dinosaurs are scared of the dark. Find Jack, Sophia and a golden egg.

1 dinosaur drawing

4 dinosaur skeletons

5 heaps of gold

6 slippy puddles

7 orange glow worms

8 large spider webs

9 ice stalactites

10 giant spiders

11 pairs of beady eyes

13 cave bats

Fun at the Beach

At the beach, the next golden egg could be hiding anywhere. Luckily, the underwater reptiles help Jack and Sophia to look, too. Can you find Jack, Sophia and another golden egg?

5 blue marine reptiles

6 red spider crabs

8 soaring sea birds

12 yellow spiral shells

15 pink starfish

Canyon Chaos

Almost there! Jack and Sophia trek through the rocky terrain in search of the last egg, but there's lots of places to search. Spot Jack and Sophia and then find the final golden egg.

5 crawling millipedes

6 stone arches

dinos having a dust bath

12 swooping blue birds

15 grumpy bees

Dinosaur Workshop

Jack and Sophia return all 12 golden eggs to the mighty T-rex. She's so grateful that she gets all her strongest dinosaur friends to fix the time machine. Can you spot Jack and Sophia?

1 hiding baby dinosaurs

4 purple dinos carrying tools

5 stone wheels

6 four-eyed spiders

7 giant, yellow bugs

8 purple fur trees

9 red feathers

10 heavy hammers

11 silver spanners

13 shiny bolts

Prehistoric Party

The mega dinosaurs have fixed the time machine and it's almost time for Jack and Sophia to leave. First, there's a prehistoric party to celebrate. Can you find Jack and Sophia?

1 purple dino doing the limbo

4 blue dinos eating flowers

5 dinos wearing face paint

6 wooden party cups

7 dinos in party hats

8 leaf-wrapped presents

9 bowls of volcano punch

10 frog balloons

11 piles of fruit

13 bowls of leaf crisps

Good work! You've helped Jack and Sophia find the 12 golden eggs and now they can return home. Now go back and see if you can find each of these cool characters and items in every scene, too.

Terry
Pterodactyl

Lucky
wishbone

Nest of
stripy eggs

Star-shaped
rock

Crystal
dinosaur skull

Line of
angry ants

Sharp
tooth

Red, poisonous
flower

How closely were you looking at each scene? Go back and see if you can spot which scene each of these items was hidden in.

Dino pulling
a funny face

4 dinos in
a boat

Dino roasting
carrots

Dino snoozing
on a branch